Henry's ball

Rod Campbell

CAMPBELL BOOKS

Into the garden

along the path

over the bricks

between the flower pots

beside the pond

under the wheelbarrow

behind the tree

through the flower bed

and *into* the air!

ISBN 0 333 61205 1

Printed in Singapore